COLLEGE LONDON

GW00658229

Piano
Grade 3

Pieces & Exercises
for Trinity College London exams

2015-2017

Published by
Trinity College London
www.trinitycollege.com

Registered in the UK
Company no. 02683033
Charity no. 1014792

Copyright © 2014 Trinity College London
First impression, June 2014

Unauthorised photocopying is illegal
No part of this publication may be copied or reproduced in any
form or by any means without the prior permission of the publisher.

Printed in Great Britain by Caligraving Ltd.

Allegro

from *Sonatina in G*

Josef Haydn
(1732-1809)

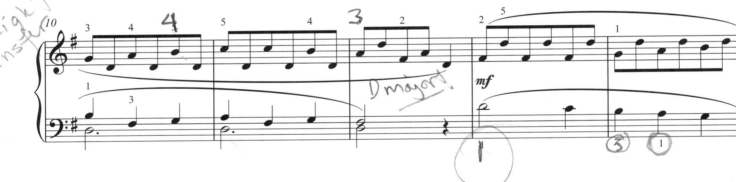

Copyright © 2014 Trinity College London

Bird-catcher's Song

from *The Magic Flute*

Arr. Pauline Hall

Wolfgang Amadeus Mozart
(1756–1791)

Allegretto [♩ = 80]

Bird-catcher's Song by Wolfgang Amadeus Mozart, arranged by Pauline Hall from 'Piano Time Opera'
© Oxford University Press 1998. Reproduced by permission. All rights reserved.

Study

op. 37 no. 34

Henry Lemoine
(1786-1854)

Copyright © 2014 Trinity College London

4

Dance of the Little Swans

from *Swan Lake*

Arr. Pauline Hall

Pyotr Ilyich Tchaikovsky
(1840–1893)

Dance of the Little Swans by Pyotr Ilyich Tchaikovsky, arranged by Pauline Hall from 'More Piano Time Classics'

© Oxford University Press 1995. Reproduced by permission. All rights reserved.

The Highway Robber

from *For Children*

Béla Bartók
(1881–1945)

© Copyright 1946 (revised 1998) by Boosey & Hawkes Music Publishers Ltd/Editio Musica Budapest

Hound Dog

Arr. Pam Wedgwood and Sam Wedgwood

Jerry Leiber (1933–2011)
and Mike Stoller (born 1933)

© Copyright 1956 Universal/MCA Music Limited. This arrangement © Copyright 2014 Universal/MCA Music Limited.
All rights reserved. International copyright secured. Used by permission of Music Sales Limited.

Sad Song

Alexander F Johnson
(born 1968)

Sad Song by Alexander Johnson from '11 Pieces for Children' © Alexander Johnson 2012.
Reproduced by permission. All rights reserved.

The Rainbow

Ray Moore
(born 1939)

Copyright © 2014 Trinity College London

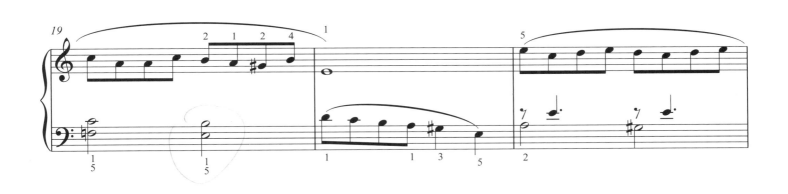

Square Dance

Hilary Tadman-Robins
(born 1947)

© Copyright 2009 Encore Publications. Reproduced by permission from the album *Just for Starters*, by Philip Ledger and Hilary Tadman-Robins. All enquiries on this piece, apart from the exams, to Encore Publications, Juglans House, Brenchley Road, Matfield, Kent TN12 7DT

Exercises

1a. Royal Visit – tone, balance and voicing

1b. A Moody Moment – tone, balance and voicing

Copyright © 2014 Trinity College London

2a. Mirrors – co-ordination

2b. Music Box – co-ordination

Copyright © 2014 Trinity College London

3a. Fine Fingers – finger & wrist strength and flexibility

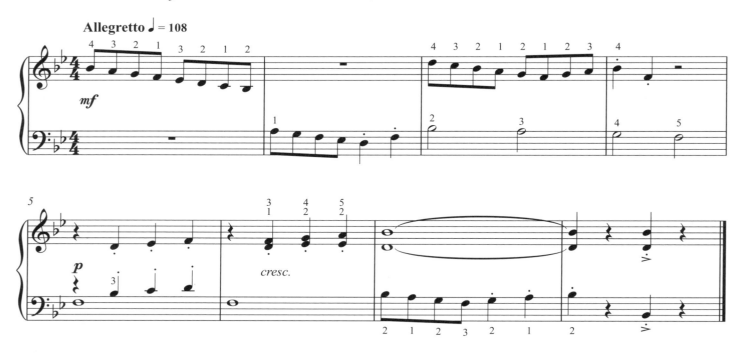

3b. Caribbean Moves – finger & wrist strength and flexibility

Copyright © 2014 Trinity College London

Teaching notes

Haydn   Allegro   page 2

This has the gracefulness of a minuet and is perhaps why the suggested metronome mark may at first seem rather conservative. A slightly quicker pulse would also be acceptable as long as the mood remains elegant. Controlling such simple left-hand figuration is deceptively difficult and will take careful listening. Some pianists may like to use a little rotary motion; others, particularly given the low dynamic, will use fingers alone. The articulation detail, as so often in this classical period, also needs attention. The second crotchet in the right hand is light, the result of a 'drop-float' action for the first two notes. But the third crotchet is a definite *staccato*, a note that needs definition, even in *piano*. In bar 4 the last note of this first phrase is a full crotchet's length only. It will be tempting to hold this and the last note of the second phrase in bar 8, but make sure they release as the left hand plays its second crotchet.

The dynamics also maintain a courtly restraint until the last phrase, but there needs to be some shaping, particularly in the more lyrical central section. Follow the tension and release of the harmony and the shape of the melody, leaning towards the third bar of each phrase in bars 9–16. You want a singing left hand here, to duet with the melody in the upper notes of the right hand. The tenor sings the duet in bars 9–12 and then the bass in bars 13–16. This is Haydn at his most gracious and aristocratic; no jokes and no real wit here, just elegant, poised writing at its most classical.

Mozart   Bird-catcher's Song   page 3

Papageno is the bird-catcher, originally played by *The Magic Flute*'s librettist, Schikaneder, who was a seasoned entertainer, usually playing for laughs. He would enter with a birdcage on his back, singing this song about catching firstly birds, then, more tricky this, women! Papageno always has a set of pipes that play those demi-semiquavers in bar 13 and elsewhere. Sometimes the actor/singer really does play them himself, and sometimes the notes are played for him in the orchestra and he just acts piping them. The timing, singing and then blowing is difficult, and this is probably exactly the same passage that will cause pianists the most trouble. Playing five ascending notes quickly, quietly and rhythmically evenly is not as easy as it looks. Let a flexible wrist slightly follow the direction of the fingers, making sure that you are over the notes before you begin to play them.

The mood is spritely, although Pauline Hall has suggested longer lines and more *legato* than you will hear from most singers in this role. The two Gs in bar 1 will be slightly detached – both, not just the first one, as implied by the ensuing slur – and the same articulation should be used in bars 16 and 18. In bars 11 and 12 it would be good to make the tenor line of the left hand *legato*, making a brief duet with the top voice. Join the A to the B in bar 11, while the little finger releases to repeat the D, and similarly in the next bar. Later on pianists will come across more part-playing that seems to divide the hand in two, and this is excellent preparation. A good arrangement of this cheerful tune.

Lemoine   Study, op. 37 no. 34   page 4

This is definitely one of the most challenging choices at this grade; a piece that demands much sophistication in both its technical execution and its musical interpretation. Lemoine belongs to that late classical / early romantic era: the pianos were still relatively light and facility and articulation were highly valued. This study demands and develops precisely that level of finger control.

It is that triplet of semiquavers that will cause all the heartache. They are marked as a three-note slur, so the final note should lightly release before the ensuing *staccato* quavers. Without interfering with the

pulse in any way, and while remaining a definite triplet – no veering towards two semiquavers and a quaver. And, naturally, without bumping the third note. Or the fourth for that matter. Did I mention that this was tricky? I would prepare by practising the same triplet pattern on each note of a descending C major scale, using the same fingers – try with 3-4-3 and 2-3-2 – with the smallest of lifts between each triplet. It would be so easy to slur into the first quaver, but it does sound different and at this level these details matter. The seconds and thirds in the left hand in bars 32–43 should be light and *staccato*. Notice that the last notes of phrases vary: some are full crotchets, but elsewhere you are requested to finish with a *staccato* quaver. All the musical detail is carefully written in and the suggested tempo is perfect to allow you to incorporate it into your interpretation to create the poise and slight melancholy of this E minor study.

Tchaikovsky   Dance of the Little Swans   page 6

It is act 2 of *Swan Lake* and four swans are dancing in unison. While their legs are moving (*points relevés*), they are making bird-like head movements and, when done well, this dance can bring the house down. It has also become famous for being used in skits, particulary by male dancers!

The left hand sets what will be an immutable pulse with a quiet *staccato*, and the right hand begins this most famous of melodies in thirds. Just before the grace notes in bar 2, the lower note of the third disappears: I would recommend moving to the 2nd finger here, using the strong fingers 1, 2, 3 for the quickest notes. The left hand will also need good finger control for its semiquavers a couple of bars later. Keep the fingers well supported from the bridge of the hand, and feel each finger moving to play its note. A small lateral wrist movement will help. There are no other dynamics noted until the last line, but instinctively there seems to be a heightening of the mood in bars 10–11 as the music moves towards A minor, with a re-balancing in the next two bars as it returns to the tonic. The arms can get involved in the last two *subito f* chords. Knowing the tune will hopefully make this an easy learn for ballet-loving pianists.

Bartók   The Highway Robber   page 7

This comes from Bartók's second volume of *For Children*, all of which are based on Slovakian folk tunes. Using folksong to teach children is a tried and tested method and still used in beginners' methods today. The balance and tunefulness of folksongs are immediately appealing, and Bartók's usual approach, followed here, is to repeat the melody with a varying accompaniment. Those of us without his genius may have harmonised the whole melody with the primary triads, but Bartók finds more distant and unexpected harmonies and the touch of A minor in the final variation is masterly; you will want to find a special colour for the *dolce*, *tranquillo* marking here.

There is a puzzling pedal direction: the pedal is marked to be lifted on the second beat of bar 3. This means that the tie in the bass will probably only last for a crotchet, but this is a better solution than blurring the melodic quavers. The small pedal marks elsewhere are to enable a *legato* between chords. The melody has a typical classical phrasing, emphasised by Bartók's accents and *tenuto* marks: one bar; one bar; two bars. Maintain this through all the variations, with that small *crescendo* into the fourth bar also implicit in the last *dolce* variation. You may like to re-distribute the two parts under this variation, taking some minims with the right hand to help the *legato* in the tenor. Of course, the fifths in bars 13–15 are easier to control in *mp* and *p* if shared between the hands.

Leiber & Stoller   Hound Dog   page 8

'You ain't nothing but a hound dog' are the opening words to this well-known rock 'n' roll hit. Elvis was not the first to sing it – that was Willie Mae 'Big Mama' Thornton – but if you look this up online, Elvis will probably be the first name that appears. You can even listen to him singing it accompanied by pictures of a variety of hounds!

This is basically a 12-bar blues, with a heavy, completely rigorous pulse, and 'swung' quavers (approximating triplets). Even the *staccato* chords have weight and length – a reluctant *staccato* perhaps, using the whole arm. The many repeated notes demand a detached articulation, which you may want to maintain throughout the piece. The only actual slur is in the penultimate bar, so there is logical reasoning behind this. But it would also be acceptable to use a *quasi-legato* for instance in bar 3, 7 and elsewhere. Notice the crotchets in the middle of bars 16 and 20, and take care over the *mf* and *f* levels, making sure the difference is audible. The rhythm in the last bar may catch out some pianists: four 'swung' quavers, with the last releasing before the third beat. Get the arm involved on the last chord for the *ff* accent. The recordings will generally play it faster than the speed suggested here, but this is a good tempo at which to work at getting the rich, firm tone required, so resist the urge to play much faster.

Johnson   Sad Song   page 9

This melancholy aria will surely win the hearts of many pianists and will be an excellent choice to develop *legato* pedalling and sound quality. It is also an opportunity to explore mood and communication; the music itself is a perfect evocation of 'sadness' and can usefully lead to discussions about what we need to think about as performers to capture that, and what we need to do to project it to our audience.

Pianists are more likely to pedal well if they understand the mechanics. The foot must hold one harmony until the next harmony is sounded. Then, and only then, can the foot lift, letting go of one set of sounds, and then depress again to catch and hold the next. The piece has clearly defined dynamic areas, which need clear differentiation – you may have a story in mind that will help this. The *mp* at the opening must be played with the final *pp* in mind, that is, not too softly. The top note of the thirds must sing as a melodic note, otherwise the sudden solo E at the end of the bar will be too prominent. The *dolce* in bar 5 suggests a solo for the first violin; a finer, less rich, sound here. No hurrying in bars 20-22; the third beat, where nothing is played, still needs to have its correct space, particularly in bar 22, as we breathe before the last phrase. The sound seems to melt away on the last line, descending to the lowest note of the piece in the left hand, as the right hand makes one last attempt to lift itself out of sadness. The final spread chord, with its sharpened third and seventh, seems to suggest that a brighter mood is not too far away.

Moore   The Rainbow   page 10

This is a wistful, haunting piece that will appeal to many pianists. You know that crock of gold is only imaginary, but it doesn't stop you dreaming!

Putting that left-hand pedal E on the second quaver of each minim adds space into the music – try playing even crotchets instead and you'll see what I mean. It allows the melody to sing without being too cluttered by the accompaniment, although you still need to help it by making a *cantabile* sound and thinking through the long lines of quavers. Take the line for a walk; find its most natural shape, responding to the direction of the harmonies, the dissonance in bar 2, the final resolution in bar 8. It is perfectly possible to play this without pedal, using a finger *legato* in the bass, but good pedalling will add an appropriate halo around the harmonies, the mist in the air from the

recent rain. Having found such a good melody, it is no surprise that Ray Moore exploits it, reprising it on the second page. Before that, make the most of the more emotive middle section, finding a warmer sound (and emotional temperature) to match the move to the plaintive sub-dominant, introduced by that most poignant of intervals, the minor 6th. In bar 16 we are directed to play *pp*, but this refers mostly to the inner parts; the melodic E in the soprano must sound through to the end of the tie. A soothing piece that is an absolute delight to play.

Tadman-Robins   Square Dance   page 12

The square dance is the American version of the quadrille, danced by four couples facing each other. The sequence of steps was often called out to the dancers, and you can imagine this happening after the introduction, as the piano 'vamps' in bars 5-8. The Grove dictionary tells us that steps from various French dances were danced, but that some were entirely American, including the tantalising 'hug 'em up tight and swing 'em like thunder'!

A strong sense of pulse is essential here – no rushing the semiquavers, or cutting short any of the rests or ties. Banjos and fiddles often accompanied these dances, and you can orchestrate the different sections in your mind to get the appropriate colours. A fiddle and cello duet in the opening, then maybe the piano sets up the heavy beats in fifths, before a wind instrument takes over the theme in bar 8. It's often better to think of dynamics in terms of instrumentation, or colour, rather than degrees of loudness, and imagining a sound helps our fingers, hands and arms find a way of making it. You can also find a physical action that helps with the syncopations; playing the *staccato* notes in a way that helps your hands to drop onto the next notes at precisely the right time. At the very end you may like to take the top note of the left-hand octave in the right hand, making it easier for the left hand to reach the final bass D. Now, take your partners...

Bartók   Rhythmic Dance   *Alfred*

This is musically straightforward, requiring decisive, rhythmic playing with a full-bodied sound. Every chord is marked with either a *staccato* or *tenuto* sign, with the former often providing ideal preparation for the latter, as you can allow gravity to help find a good sound on the held chords. It would be very easy to tighten the muscles and make a hard tone; instead, think of the poise and buoyancy of dancers as they jump and land with flexing ankles that allow them to take off again. The piece is *forte* throughout, but it is a vibrant *forte*, no stamping. Towards the end of each half, I would recommend coming back a little in dynamic, so that there is a sense of building into the very end of each phrase. So the last quaver in bars 4 and 9 can be nearer *mf*, then there can be a subtle *crescendo* through the subsequent bars. This is one of those pieces that keeps its energy directed towards the very last note, and in fact these cadence bars, bars 5 and 10, are additional to requirements; they drive the point home. You reach C major in bar 4, then bar 5 says 'yes, I've really got here'. Next a series of sequences, in A minor, then G major, then the material is shortened, but passes through F major and E minor, finally taking us back to the tonic, D minor. 'Yes, we've really got here' then shouts the final bar. A tempo of 132 crotchets a minute will capture the energy of this dance.

Diabelli	Bagatelle		*Alfred*

We usually translate 'bagatelle' as a 'trifle', an inconsequential, whimsical piece, usually quite short. Perhaps the most famous bagatelle is Beethoven's *Für Elise*, although his cycle of bagatelles, op. 126, was actually his last major composition for the piano, with the six pieces seeming to form one longer work. Another of Beethoven's most famous works was of course inspired by one Mr Anton Diabelli...

Here Diabelli is in teaching mode, but the result is delightful: spirited, energetic and classically balanced. Articulation must be bright and crisp, with an unwavering pulse until the *poco rit.* in bar 16. *Forte* here should be really *forte*, with the *piano* a complete contrast. Practise the accompaniment alone to ensure that it also observes the dynamics. Play the appoggiatura (leaning note) in bar 3 as an acciaccatura (crushed note) – the former would sound too fussy in this context. The *staccato* direction in bar 9 applies to the quavers, not the crotchet, but note that the last treble note in bar 12 will be a *staccato* quaver. The recapitulation is *p* and remains *p* until the last two bars, so make sure that the *sf* is within that dynamic. I would suggest playing the final quavers with a little more length than elsewhere, just to finish the piece with attitude. Crotchet at around 88 is a good speed for this trifle.

Goedicke	Sonatina		*OUP*

Alexander Goedicke (now more usually spelt Gedike) was a Russian pianist and composer who became one of the piano professors at the Moscow Conservatoire, although I doubt that this piece was written with those pianists in mind! Nevertheless it is ideal teaching material, with some robust chordal playing, neat fingerwork and snippets of melody above an Alberti bass accompaniment. Good use of the arms will help produce the strong, accented chords, with a quick change to precise fingers for the following semiquavers. These will sound good if they *diminuendo* into the next *p* bar. A supple wrist will aid the sound and phrasing in the more lyrical bars 5-8, helping the right hand lift at the ends of the small slurs without clipping and accenting the final quavers. Similarly in the bass, some gentle rotary movement will help to keep the quavers smooth and gentle – an accompanying *mf*, which in reality probably amounts to a *mp*, allowing the melodic fragments to project without pushing the sound.

The tempo needs to be reasonably steady to accommodate the different sections; somewhere around 112 crotchets a minute allows space for the melodic material and has enough momentum to give the opening energy. You may want to ease into the recapitulation, taking a fraction extra time in bar 12 before the surprise of the *f subito* in the next bar. There is plenty of dynamic detail written into the piece, but do also analyse the harmonies and shape the music in response to this. Bars 2 and 4 seem very similar and both are marked *piano*, but bar 2 ends on the dominant and is halfway through a longer phrase that culminates in a perfect cadence in bar 4. Understanding those elements of tension and release is fundamental to so much music-making.

Hengeveld	Cha-cha-cha		*Broekmans*

This comes from a book of dances called *Mélodie en Rythme*, which also contains a habanera, a couple of foxtrots, an Argentinian tango and an English waltz. Before piano teachers had Norton, Milne, Cornick et al to use for post-exam relaxing, Hengeveld was someone I often turned to. The suggested tempo is quite challenging at this grade, and a speed in the low 70s is perfectly acceptable. The cha-cha-cha is a Cuban dance with lots of hip movement and has a more relaxed mood than some of the other Latin-American dances.

Hengeveld's cha-cha-cha is more spiky – elbows rather than hips perhaps – and the pulse must be immutable throughout. Thanks to the internet, it will be easy for pianists to watch the cha-cha-cha being danced to get a sense of the movements involved. The length of the left-hand crotchet chords should all be the same, so not too long for that first one, and the right-hand notes should all be detached, albeit with crotchets longer than quavers. The *diminuendo* in bar 15 may at first seem counter-intuitive, so will need practising. The only slurs are in the left hand in bar 4 and its later repeat, and notice that the right hand maintains its *staccato* in these places. The final notes in the right hand are also marked with a slur, although this is not essential for small hands. Make a *crescendo* in this last bar – it is the sort of piece that wants to end with a kick, and not with elegance!

Jírovec	Waltz no. 1		*Boosey*

Today we often make a link between music and maths, but in earlier times many composers, largely perhaps through pressure from their families, studied law. Jírovec – pronounced 'gyrowetz' – was one of these. A Bohemian composer, he met both Mozart and Haydn, and in fact the impresario Salomon commissioned symphonies from Jírovec as well as Haydn while they were both visiting London.

Repeats are required in the exam. The dynamic indications in the second half are probably best left as they are both times, but you could perhaps reverse the *p/f* in the first section during the repeat. Or you could try putting a little more emphasis on the bass the second time around. Nothing too obvious; Charles Rosen in *The Classical Style* tells us that the very fact that we are hearing something for the second time already means that it is different and we do not need to do much more. A touch of pedal in the three *legato* bars towards the end will help the *crescendo* and makes the return to the drier texture in the penultimate bar quite witty, as the sudden injection of intensity is deflated. Given the *vivo* direction – try this at around 144 crotchets to a minute – it will be enough to think of active, light fingers in the right hand, rather than trying to detach all the quavers. There is one tricky moment at the end of bar 4, where the right hand needs to make quite a leap in a new dynamic. Make sure you phrase off the first four quavers of that bar and ease into the return of the theme if necessary, so that it sounds natural, musically shaped and not grabbed.

Martin	Jack-Junior		*Bosworth*

Philip Martin is a pianist, composer and teacher, so who better to write pieces for teaching the piano? Among his compositions are three piano concertos as well as a host of smaller works for solo piano. His website tells us that tone production is important in his teaching, and this clever piece continually asks us to change articulation, dynamic and emphasis. Both cheeky and challenging, but great fun when it is securely in the brain and the fingers. A tempo of around ♩ = 126 will be lively but allow space for all the about-turns.

Details to note: the crotchet in the right hand of bar 5 compared to the quaver in bar 12 – that is really sneaky! The *sf* notes should always be within the dynamic framework, so they both come under a general *piano* dynamic, so gentle accents only. The comma at the end of bar 7 is to point the structure, the repeat of the opening material, but a tone up; try not to allow it to turn the 3/8 bar into a bar of 4/8. Then there's another sneaky moment at the end of bar 22, where we expect the left hand to be nearer the right hand geographically, whereas it actually continues its previous descent into the bass clef. The C in bar 24 could easily be played by the right hand, but the smooth journey from left to right in bars 25-26 will take some careful listening. Basically the dynamic structure revolves around a contrast between *f* and *p*, with small swells. It may be useful to highlight the lines in colours: something pale for *p*, and something vibrant for *f*. Whoever Jack-Junior is, he is a bit of a prankster if this music is anything to go by!

Schubert Ecossaise *Faber*

Schubert wrote so many of these short dances, especially ländlers and waltzes, and it is often remarkable to see what he can do with 16 bars. This rather tender piece is over so quickly that it would be better to play the repeats in the exam, and for those pianists who can comfortably reach the pedal some pedalling would also add warmth to the texture.

The écossaise, a Scottish dance, was written in duple time, as is this one, but this sounds more Schubert than Scottish. Learn the left hand as triads, noticing that bars 4 and 6 are the same, despite looking so different, and understanding the significance of the diminished 7th in the fifth bar. When playing the melody, allow the wrist to follow the shape of the phrase, keeping it supple and the sound rounded. The release of the quavers at the end of the two-bar slurs must always be graceful; listen carefully to make sure the last note does not bump as you move to the next position – especially important in the second half. Schubert's use of major and minor keys is particularly potent and we sometimes talk of the minor representing a depressing reality, while his forays into quiet major echoes seem to be more like a dream of how things could be. Here too there is a definite increase in tension as the second part moves to A minor in *mf* then *f,* and something so touchingly consoling about the next *p* bar, as it returns us to C major. Even in 16 bars, genius will out. A metronome mark of around 100 works well.

Schumann Erster Verlust *Peters*

This poignant piece is usually translated as 'First Loss' and will appeal to those musicians who respond to more melancholy, lyrical works. Schumann wrote a collection of piano pieces for young pianists and a similar collection of songs for young singers, but he has not compromised here and rightly expects a young person's imaginative response to be equal to the considerable fluid demands of the music.

For much of the time the left hand lies close to the right, commenting on and sympathising with the melody's story of loss. Although they sit close together, make sure we still hear the treble notes as the more melodic, with the G–E in bar 2 as a gentle response rather than an interruption. The initial *fp* is troublesome; an accent here seems too disruptive. Instead use an agogic accent, giving the G a little more space and richness, rather than playing it in an isolated *forte*. There is a section of three-part playing in bars 21–25 which will take careful management. I prefer to take the mezzo A in bar 24 with the left hand, leaving the right free to begin the recapitulation, this time without a *fp*, but other re-arrangements are also possible. These bars give a sense of a build-up of grief as one part after another iterates the theme. The real *forte* comes at the end: this sudden, brief release of anger at the loss is quite shocking after the tenderness elsewhere, but keep the sound full, not hard. Some pedal would be useful, but is not essential, and the suggested metronome mark is rather fast to achieve all the subtleties Schumann indicates, so something in the high 70s or 80s is acceptable.

Tanner A Fish can Whistle *Spartan*

There are several pieces by Mark Tanner in the syllabus (see Grades 2 and 4), all with imaginative titles. Whether or not fish can whistle I shall leave others to decide, but there are other questions posed by the piece to which I can propose solutions.

The accompanying crotchet chords are marked *mezzo piano* and *staccato*. This suggests that they should be in the background, but played crisply enough to add vitality to the whole. Although there are no slurs above the melody, I would suggest generally playing this *legato*, with the crotchets held for their full length. This will demand some nifty fingerwork in places, such as bar 6, where the left-hand

chord must release promptly for the melody to re-play one of its notes. Another small conundrum is the use of dotted quaver–semiquaver, as in bar 2, but it has long been traditional for composers writing in a basically 'swung' style, where quavers become triplets, to notate the first and third of a group of triplets like this. It would sound too clipped within what is a relaxed piece, to suddenly subdivide the crotchet into four. The accented chords at the end of each section sound like the brass section commenting on proceedings – a full sound here and not overly spiky. The character is one of sauntering down the road, or along the stream, jauntily whistling as you swing your fins!

Teaching notes written by Pamela Lidiard

Key

A solid line denotes a piece within this book.

A dotted line denotes a piece from the alternative list.